Daily *warm-ups*

SPELLING AND GRAMMAR

J. WESTON
WALCH
PUBLISHER
Portland, Maine

1   2   3   4   5   6   7   8   9   10
ISBN 0-8251-4322-5
Copyright © 2002
J. Weston Walch, Publisher
P.O. Box 658 • Portland, Maine 04104-0658
www.walch.com
Printed in the United States of America

The *Daily Warm-Ups* series is a wonderful way to turn extra classroom minutes into valuable learning time. The 180 quick activities—one for each day of the school year—review, practice, and teach spelling and grammar points. These daily activities may be used at the very beginning of class to get students into learning mode, near the end of class to make good educational use of that transitional time, in the middle of class to shift gears between lessons—or whenever else you have minutes that now go unused. In addition to providing students with structure and focus, they are a natural path to other classroom activities involving spelling and grammar.

Daily Warm-Ups are easy-to-use reproducibles—simply photocopy the day's activity and distribute it. Or make a transparency of the activity and project it on the board. You may want to use the activities for extra-credit points, as a check on retention of spelling and grammar you have already taught, or even as mini-lessons on topics that students have not studied recently.

However you choose to use them, *Daily Warm-Ups* are a convenient and useful supplement to your regular lesson plans. Make every minute of your class time count!

Synonyms are words that mean the same thing, like *cool* and *chilly*. Brainstorm eight synonyms for the verb *walk*. Write a sentence for each synonym. Explain the shades of difference in meaning of the eight different verbs.

Change from verbs to
adjectives
angry, mad, furious, agitated
upset

1

Some linking verbs show a state of being: *Manny **is** in the media center*, for example. Other linking verbs link the subject of the sentence with another word: *Lisa **was** the winner of the spelling bee*.

Action verbs show physical action (*Lisa **won** the spelling bee*), mental action (*Manny **daydreamed** in the media center*), or ownership (*Sandi **has** a new scooter*).

2

Write a descriptive paragraph with four to six linking verbs. After completing your paragraph, substitute action verbs for the linking verbs. Write the action verbs above the linking verbs. Change other words in the paragraph as needed.

Make up a word search puzzle

containing ten action verbs. Exchange papers with a partner and solve each other's puzzles. Exchange papers again for scoring.

3

A noun names a person, a place, a thing, or an idea. A **common noun** names any person, place, thing, or idea (*school, town, singer*). A **proper noun** names a specific person, place, thing, or idea and is always capitalized (*Hughes Middle School, Los Angeles, Britney Spears*).

List three common nouns related to objects in your classroom. Then list three proper nouns related to your classroom.

4

Common Nouns	Proper Nouns

Make a list of five common nouns of five or more letters. Jumble the letters in the words and make an answer key. Exchange papers with a partner to unscramble the nouns. Write a sentence for each noun you've unscrambled. Return papers for scoring.

An adjective modifies a noun or a pronoun. A **descriptive adjective** answers the question *What kind?*

Cluster four descriptive adjectives to describe your three favorite animals. Draw pictures or cartoons of the animals next to the adjectives.

6

Write the names of five friends or family members. Surround each name with five vivid descriptive adjectives.

Brainstorm six descriptive adjectives to describe one object in your classroom. Exchange papers with a partner and write the noun you think the list of adjectives describes.

8

An adverb modifies a verb, an adjective, or another adverb. An adverb answers the questions *Where? When? How?* or *How much/to what extent?*

Write five sentences with adverbs that modify verbs. Write which question about verbs each adverb answers. Circle the verbs. Underline the adverbs.

© 2002 J. Weston Walch, Publisher

Brainstorm ten common nouns.

Next to each common noun, write a proper noun
that relates to it. Here's an example: common noun:
school; proper noun: *Riverview Middle School*.

Common Nouns

Proper Nouns

10

Write a short paragraph with ten proper nouns. (Remember, proper nouns name a specific person, place, thing, or idea and are always capitalized.) Highlight the proper nouns.

Then substitute **personal pronouns** for the proper nouns. Personal pronouns include *I*, *me*, *mine*, *we*, *us*, *our*, *ours*, *you*, *your*, *yours*, *he*, *him*, *his*, *she*, *her*, *hers*, *it*, *its*, *they*, *them*, *their*, and *theirs*.

11

© 2002 J. Weston Walch, Publisher

Make a list of ten different places you've visited or would like to visit. Surround each place-name with at least three vibrant descriptive adjectives. Draw a star over your three favorite places.

12

Write five sentence fragments,

or incomplete sentences. Turn each fragment into a complete sentence. How are the complete sentences different from sentence fragments? Is it ever acceptable to use sentence fragments?

13

Use each of these irregular verbs
(*choose, drive, know, swim, take, go, bring, burst*) in a different sentence. Write your sentences in the present or past tense. Write the verb tense above each verb.

14

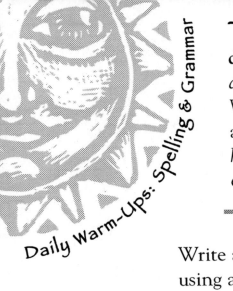

There are four types of sentences:

declarative, which makes a statement: *Clara works after school;* **interrogative,** which asks a question: *Where does Clara work?* **imperative,** which makes a request or gives a command: *Don't forget your homework;* and **exclamatory,** which expresses strong emotion: *She finishes her homework during her breaks!*

Write a paragraph about your favorite sport or hobby using at least one of each sentence type: declarative (*D*), interrogative (*INT*), imperative (*IMP*), or exclamatory (*EX*). Label each sentence type.

15

Think of words you can substitute for the following: *fireman, mailman, salesman, businessman,* and *chairman.* Use words that include both men and women. Write a sentence for each revised word.

16

Quotations, or what people say, can be direct or indirect. In **direct quotations,** a person's exact words are used and those words are set off with quotation marks: *Jack said, "The match won't start on time if it rains."*

Indirect quotations give the meaning of what a person said, but not necessarily his or her exact words. Indirect quotations do not use quotation marks: *Jack said that the game would start late if it rains tonight.*

Write a humorous dialogue with at least six direct quotations. Then rewrite the dialogue, changing three of the direct quotations into indirect quotations.

17

Write five sentences showing five different uses for capital letters. Explain why you used capitals in each instance.

18

A proper adjective is an adjective that is formed from a proper noun, such as *Australian* wolfhound, *Belgian* chocolates, *Republican* convention.

Use six proper nouns and two proper adjectives in a paragraph about a day you spent with friends. Use your imagination. Circle the proper nouns. Underline the proper adjectives.

19

A helping verb is used with a main verb (*Isabelle **is** holding the gerbil; Seth **has** listened to that CD three times today.*) Common helping verbs include *is, must, have, will, would, should, has,* and *do*.

Write a letter to the editor about an issue that concerns you. Include at least six helping verbs. Underline the helping verbs. Circle the main verbs.

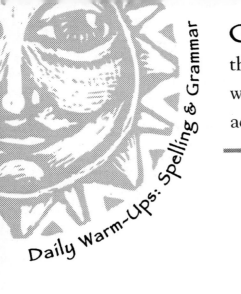

Create an adjective wheel. Write the name of your favorite food in the middle of the wheel. On the eight spokes of the wheel, write adjectives that describe the food.

A **preposition shows** the relationship between a noun or a pronoun and another word in the sentence. Some common prepositions are listed below.

about	before	for	off	under
above	between	from	on	with
after	by	in	through	
at	during	of	to	

A **prepositional phrase** starts with a preposition and includes the **object of the preposition** and any words that modify the object: *The meal **in the oven** smells delicious.*

Write four sentences containing prepositional phrases. Underline the prepositions.

A preposition always has an object. Sometimes, a preposition can have more than one object. In that case, the prepositional phrase has a compound object of the preposition. *Lee gave the invitations* **to LaDonna and Hannah.** *Everyone except* **Tom and Alicia** *went to the game.*

Write three sentences with compound objects of the preposition. In each sentence, underline the preposition, and circle the compound object of the preposition.

23

A simple sentence has one subject and one verb. A **compound sentence** is made up of at least two simple sentences that are joined together, usually with a comma and a **coordinating conjunction.** The coordinating conjunctions are *and, but, or,* and *yet.*

Two simple sentences: *Carmen is a drummer. Her band is playing at Central Auditorium tomorrow.*

One compound sentence: *Carmen is a drummer, **and** her band is playing at Central Auditorium tomorrow.*

24

Write four simple sentences about an activity you enjoy. Then turn the simple sentences into two compound sentences.

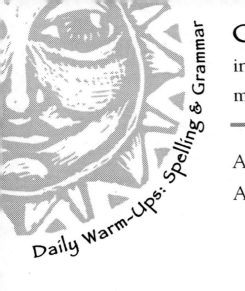

Change the masculine pronouns

in the following sentences so that they reflect both men and women. Give two solutions for each sentence.

A senator gives up his privacy when he runs for office.

A doctor studies for many years to learn his profession.

25

A **prefix** is a word part attached at the beginning of a word that changes the meaning of the core word. Complete the chart below by adding a prefix that means "not" to the core word.

Core Words	Prefix Meaning "not"	New Word
balance		
legal		
mature		
polite		
rational		
sane		

26

The prefixes above are all related to the prefix *in-*. They change depending on the spelling of the word they are added to. Write a spelling rule that tells when to use which form of the prefix.

Provide two examples of proper nouns for each category: organizations, teams, holidays, historical events, planets, and stars or constellations.

27

All complete sentences have two parts: a **subject** and a **predicate.** The subject is who or what the sentence is about. The predicate tells something about the subject and always contains a verb.

Write a one-paragraph review of your favorite television program. Underline subjects once and predicates twice.

28

Write separate sentences for each of these troublesome pairs of modifiers: *bad/badly*, *good/well*, *slow/slowly*. Explain what each word means and how it differs from the other word in the pair.

29

Look at the words in bold type in this sentence: ***Eight weird** animals visited the **sheik.*** These words are exceptions to which spelling rule? State the first part of this spelling rule, and give at least five examples of words that follow the rule.

30

Study this spelling rule: If a word ends with a silent *e*, drop the *e* before adding a suffix that begins with a vowel (for example, *state: stating*). Write three other words that follow this rule.

31

These words are exceptions to a spelling rule: *judgment*, *truly*, *argument*, and *ninth*. Write the spelling rule and give three examples of words that are *not* exceptions.

32

Add a suffix to these words ending in *y*: *hurry* (use a past tense verb); *lady* (make it plural); *beauty* (change it to an adjective); *happy* (change it to a noun).

What does the spelling of these pairs of words have in common: *prefer/preferred, forget/forgettable, refer/referred, admit/admittance?*

Write three more examples of similar words.

34

An appositive renames or explains a noun or a pronoun: *Tran,* **the captain of the soccer team,** *went home sick today.* Appositives are usually set off by commas.

Write six sentences with appositives. Highlight the appositives and underline the word or words they describe. Circle the commas.

35

© 2002 J. Weston Walch, Publisher

Verbs show action or state of being. Verbs also tell *when* the action or state of being happened by which tense is used. Here are some examples using the verb *run: Wyatt **runs** every day after school. Yesterday Wyatt **ran** for the bus. Tomorrow Wyatt **will run** in the 5K race. Wyatt **has run** in two marathons.*

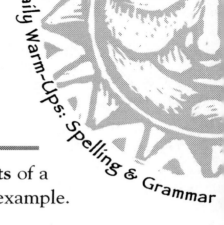

All the verb tenses are formed using the **principal parts** of a verb. Fill in the chart of principal parts following the example.

Present	Past	Past Participle
start	started	started
yell		
stop		

Write a spelling rule about forming the past participle based on your chart above.

36

Write the past tense of these irregular verbs: *dive*, *draw*, *hurt*, *freeze*, *read*, *shake*, and *hit*.

Now write a short, short story using all the words. Underline all the irregular verbs.

37

Write the past participles (*have*
form: *I have* **walked**) of the following irregular verbs:
freeze, grow, become, do, choose, know, and *eat.*

Now use each of the past participles you wrote above
in a paragraph about something or someone you know.

38

Complete the principal parts

chart for the following irregular verbs.

Present	Past	Past Participle
	rode	
	saw	
	shook	
	shrank	
	spoke	
	swam	
	threw	
	wrote	

39

Brainstorm a list of fifteen regular verbs.

Write sentences for ten of them in the past tense.
Underline the regular verbs.

40

Write directions to a familiar place using at least five prepositional phrases. Underline the prepositional phrases and circle the prepositions.

41

Write sentences for these nouns: *binoculars, pliers, scissors, shears,* and *trousers.*

42

Did you use singular or plural verbs?

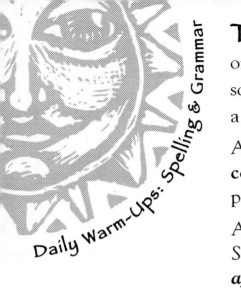

The subject of a sentence is who or what the sentence is about. The **predicate** tells something about the subject and always contains a verb.

A **simple subject** contains one noun or pronoun; a **compound subject** contains more than one noun or pronoun: *Sal and Ben work at the bookstore.*

A **compound predicate** contains more than one verb: *Sal **works** at the bookstore and **practices** violin after school.*

Write two sentences about a place you have visited. Write one sentence with a compound subject (*CS*) and one with a compound predicate (*CP*).

43

A clause is a group of words that has a subject and a verb and is used as part of a sentence. There are two types of clauses: **independent (or main)** and **dependent (or subordinate).**

Independent clauses can stand alone; they make sense by themselves and express a complete thought (*He ate a sandwich.*). An independent clause can be written as a simple sentence. Dependent clauses cannot stand alone and do not express a complete thought (*After he had studied for an hour*). They need an independent clause to complete their meaning.

A sentence with one independent clause and at least one dependent clause is called a **complex sentence:** *After he had studied for an hour, he ate a sandwich.*

Write three simple sentences about an activity you enjoy. Then change each simple sentence to make it part of a complex sentence.

Subordinate conjunctions introduce subordinate, or dependent, clauses. The subordinating conjunctions follow.

after	because	than	where
although	before	though	wherever
as	if	unless	while
as if	in order that	until	
as long as	since	when	
as soon as	so that	whenever	

Write five sentences containing subordinate clauses. Underline the subordinating conjunctions.

45

A compound-complex sentence

contains at least two independent clauses and at least one dependent clause: *Because Grace was so tired, she did not study last night, and she failed the social studies test this morning.*

Write three compound-complex sentences about school or after-school activities.

46

Make these Latin and Greek words plural by changing the final *i* to another letter: *crisis, parenthesis, analysis, basis,* and *diagnosis.*

Write a spelling rule to explain what you did.

47

Write a paragraph about going someplace with a friend. Use at least four compound subjects. Make one of the subjects in each sentence a pronoun. Write *SP* above the subject pronouns.

48

Do you use a singular or plural verb after these phrases: *one of those who; one of the things that; one of the people who?*

Write two sentences for each of these expressions. Underline the verbs.

49

Write a sentence for each of these action verbs: *say, walk, run,* and *cook.*

Now rewrite the sentences using more interesting action verbs.

50

Write a paragraph about school using three verbs that express mental action (MA) and two verbs that show physical action (PA). Underline the verbs and label them using the abbreviations.

51

Sentences can be in the **passive voice** or the **active voice.** The passive voice shows the subject being acted on. The passive voice uses a form of the verb *be* plus the past participle of the main verb: *The team **was applauded** by the PTA.* The active voice shows the subject acting: *The PTA **applauded** the team.*

Write three sentences in the passive voice.

_____

_____

_____

_____

_____

_____

Now change the sentences to the active voice.

52

Change the following expressions so that they are gender-neutral (are neither specifically male or female): *delivery man, may the best man win, policeman, stewardess, waitress,* and *watchman.* Use each gender-neutral expression in a sentence. Why is it better to use such language?

53

Connotations are the feelings people associate with a word. Make lists of the connotations you think of when you see each of the following words: *stubborn*, *blunt*, *cunning*, *delicate*, and *muscular*. Write at least four connotations for each word.

54

Think about more direct terms for these euphemisms: *passed away*, *offender*, *unmotivated*, *cautious*, and *waste disposal facility*. Write sentences using each of the direct terms.

Why is it usually better to use the more direct terms? When are euphemisms appropriate?

55

Think of ten nouns that can be used as adjectives (for example: *noun—chicken; noun used as adjective—chicken sandwich*). Write each adjective and a noun it modifies (*chicken sandwich*).

56

Write a paragraph about one of your best friends. Underline and label the following parts of speech: noun (*N*), verb (*V*), adjective (*ADJ*), adverb (*ADV*), pronoun (*PRO*).

57

Use each of these words in two

different sentences as two different parts of speech: *paper, today, musical, dance,* and *taste.* Write the part of speech above the word.

58

Participles are verb forms that act as adjectives. There are two kinds of participles: **present participles** and **past participles.** Present participles are formed by adding *-ing* to the plain form of a verb: *The **snarling** dog leaped at the cat.* Past participles are usually formed by adding *-d* or *-ed* to the end of the plain form of the verb: *The **embarrassed** owner tugged at the leash.* A **participial phrase** is made up of a participle and its related words: ***Snarling at the cat,** the dog jumped over the fence.*

Using five participial phrases, write a paragraph about a family member. Highlight the participial phrases and circle the commas surrounding them.

59

A gerund is a verb form used as a noun: **Volunteering** *is an important part of his life.* Write ten gerunds that describe something you like to do.

Now use five of the gerunds you wrote in sentences. Circle the gerunds.

60

Copy a short paragraph from one of your textbooks. Label the sentences simple (S), compound (C), complex (CX), or compound-complex (CCX). Explain why you labeled each sentence as you did.

61

Imagine that you're writing a set of instructions for doing or making something you enjoy. Write a paragraph telling the reader how to do something, being sure to include transition words that tell the order in which to do the steps. Common chronological order transition words include *first*, *second*, *third*, *next*, *after*, *finally*, and *at the end*. Circle the transition words in your instructions.

62

Write a print ad for a historical site you have visited or would like to visit. Label your sentences simple (S), compound (C), complex (CX), or compound-complex (CCX).

What type of sentence is most common in your ad? Why do you think that is?

63

Write a short television commercial for your favorite ice-cream flavor. Use at least eight descriptive adjectives. Underline the adjectives.

64

Write sentences using semicolons before these words and commas after the words: *consequently, finally, furthermore, however, in fact, meanwhile, otherwise,* and *therefore.*

65

Write a telephone conversation between you and a friend making plans to go out on the weekend. Use quotation marks in your dialogue. Remember to start a new paragraph every time the speaker changes.

66

Attach each prefix to a common noun: *anti-*, *post-*, *extra-*, *super-*, *co-*, *non-*, and *semi-*. Do not use hyphens. Use a dictionary if you need help.

67

Sometimes a phrase or a clause is intended to describe one thing in a sentence but appears to describe another. This is called a **dangling modifier.** *Gazing in the window, the boots caught Ellie's eye.* It was not the boots gazing, but Ellie. This can be corrected by placing the modifier next to what it is modifying: *Gazing in the window, Ellie saw the boots.*

Write four silly sentences with dangling modifiers. Then rewrite the sentences, correcting the placement of the modifiers.

68

Write six compound-complex sentences. Underline the independent clauses once and the dependent clauses twice.

69

Imagine that you're the vice-principal. Make up school schedules for three students. Each student takes five subjects (at least one foreign language and a history course with a number after it). Circle the school subjects that need capitals.

70

Correct the spelling of these tricky words: *collige*, *plege*, *knowlige*, *milage*, and *privlege*. Use each word in a sentence and underline the trouble spot.

71

Homonyms are words that sound
the same but have different meanings and spellings.
Write sentences for these pairs of homonyms: *sea/see*,
sail/sale, *grown/groan*, *rain/reign*, *weak/week*. Use both
homonyms of the pair in one sentence.

72

Write the plurals of these words: *alumna*, *cactus*, *criterion*, *curriculum*, and *octopus*. Use a dictionary if you need help.

Use the plurals of the words in sentences and highlight them.

73

Use these pairs of commonly confused words in sentences: *adapt/adopt*; *advice/advise*; *affect/effect*; *allusion/illusion*. Use a different sentence for each word. You may use a dictionary to check meanings.

74

Some words are misused or confused because they sound similar. Define each word below, and write an example showing it used correctly.

lie/lay   altogether/all together   sit/set

75

Use each of the following words in a different sentence to show the correct meaning: *hear/here*; *right/rite/write*; *wail/whale*; *stake/steak*.

Write sentences to show how to use each of these expressions correctly: *abstain from*; *capable of*; *contend with*; *disappointed in*; *refrain from*; *succeed in*; *wait on*. Underline the expression in each sentence.

77

Make a list of fifteen slang words you and your friends use. Next to each word, write the standard English meaning.

78

Change each cliché into a fresh expression: *a chip off the old block, crying shame, as happy as a lark, fine and dandy, burn the midnight oil, last straw, makes my blood boil, sink or swim.* Use at least five of the revised expressions in sentences.

79

A simile is a comparison of two unlike things, using the word *like* or *as*. Robert Burns's line My *luve* [love] *is like a red, red rose* is an example of a simile. The narrator compares a person to a flower.

Write five sentences containing similes to describe people you know. Highlight the similes.

80

A metaphor is a comparison of two unlike things *not* using the word *like* or *as*. Two examples are found in these lines from John Boyle O'Reilly's poem "A White Rose": O, *the red rose is a falcon/And the white rose is a dove.* In this case, flowers are compared to birds.

Write five sentences containing metaphors to describe familiar objects. Highlight the metaphors.

81

© 2002 J. Weston Walch, Publisher

Imagine you're an English teacher. Why would you mark each of these expressions incorrect in a student's essay: *in view of the fact that; might of; could of; between you and I; past history?*

82

Do you know how to use commas with each of these comma rules: series; after introductory words; with transitional words; and after two or more introductory prepositional phrases? Write a sentence showing each rule in use. Circle the commas.

83

Circle the trouble spots in each

of these spelling words: *acknowledgment, bankruptcy, budget, calendar, changeable, commitment, deterrent,* and *correspondence*. Write a sentence using each spelling word, highlighting the word.

84

See how many words you can find hidden in these commonly misspelled words: *embarrass, equipped, forfeit, grammar, hierarchy,* and *knowledge.* Write a memory device using the smaller words to help you remember how to spell the longer words.

85

Write an e-mail to a friend about a movie you liked or disliked. Use all of these commonly misspelled words: *rapport*, *recommend*, *relevant*, *scenario*, and *unanimous*. Use a dictionary if you need to check meanings. Underline the words in your e-mail. Write a draft of your e-mail below.

86

Write a short business letter using these verbs often used in the business world: *brainstorm, communicate, concur, demonstrate, develop, energize, facilitate, motivate,* and *persuade*. Underline the verbs. Remember to use correct business letter form, including correct sender's address, correct recipient's address, and appropriate greeting and closing.

87

Write a jingle for a favorite food product. Use strong action verbs and vivid descriptive adjectives. Underline the verbs and circle the adjectives.

88

List five words that can be used as at least two different parts of speech. Write a sentence for each word. Explain how each word is used in the sentence.

Write three sentences, each using a colon in a different way: to introduce a list, to introduce a long quotation, to introduce an explanation. Circle the colons in your sentences.

90

Think up your own memory tricks to help you remember how to spell the commonly misspelled words below. Write your memory trick next to each word.

misspell

banana

tragedy

government

loneliness

ninety

parallel

excitement

91

Write sentences using these commonly misused words correctly. After each pair of sentences, explain how the two words are different.

beside/besides   can/may   compare/contrast

92

Write the plural of each word below.

calf _____

elf _____

half _____

leaf _____

loaf _____

shelf _____

thief _____

Write a rule to explain what you did to make these words plural.

93

Write the plural of each word below.

box _____

fox _____

lunch _____

mess _____

tax _____

waltz _____

Write a rule to explain what you did to make these words plural.

94

List six concrete nouns and six **abstract nouns** below.

Concrete Nouns	Abstract Nouns

Explain the difference between concrete and abstract nouns.

95

Write a press release about your

favorite sports star or recording artist. Use at least ten vibrant descriptive adjectives in your press release. Highlight the adjectives.

96

Some linking verbs can also be used as action verbs. Use each of the following verbs in sentences as both linking verbs (*LV*) and action verbs (*AV*): *smell, taste, grow, sound,* and *feel*. Label all the verbs using the abbreviations.

97

© 2002 J. Weston Walch, Publisher

Write a rhymed or an unrhymed poem describing something you admire in nature. Use three actions verbs (*AV*) and five descriptive adjectives (*DA*). Underline and label the verbs and adjectives, using the abbreviations.

98

Besides a subject and a verb, a sentence sometimes needs a **complement** to complete the meaning of the sentence. One kind of complement is a **direct object,** which always follows an action verb.

Ryan built does not express a complete thought, but adding a direct object completes the meaning: *Ryan built sand castles.* A direct object answers the question *What?* or *Whom?*

Write three sentences containing direct objects.

99

Some sentences need a complement to complete their meaning. One type of complement is a direct object. Another type is an **indirect object,** which, like a direct object, also follows an action verb. An indirect object answers the question *To what?* or *To whom?* but does not use the word *to: Suki gave **Luis** the card.* In this sentence, *card* is the direct object of the verb *gave* (What did Suki give?), and *Luis* is the indirect object (To whom did Suki give the card?). If a sentence contains an indirect object, it must also contain a direct object.

100

Write three sentences that contain an indirect object. Label the indirect objects (*IO*) and the direct object (*DO*).

The following do not express complete statements: *Ryan is. Johnna felt.* A complement is needed to complete the meaning.

A **predicate nominative** is such a complement. It is a noun or a pronoun that follows a *linking verb* and renames, identifies, or explains the subject. *Ryan is a great* **athlete.**

Another complement that follows a linking verb is a **predicate adjective.** A predicate adjective describes the subject. *Johnna felt* **unhappy.**

Write two sentences containing predicate nominatives (*PN*) and two sentences containing predicate adjectives (*PA*).

101

Wake up these tired adjectives by using more lively synonyms: *fabulous*, *nice*, *spectacular*, *good*, and *fine*. Write sentences about people or places familiar to you, using the livelier adjectives. Highlight the adjectives.

102

Write an ad for a rock concert using at least two declarative sentences (*D*), two exclamatory sentences (*E*), and one interrogative sentence (*I*). Use the abbreviations to label your sentences.

103

© 2002 J. Weston Walch, Publisher

Write six clichés you've heard people use. Rewrite the clichés in standard English.

104

People often speak in hackneyed, or overused, phrases. Write three hackneyed similes about the weather (*It's as hot as an oven.*). Then write three more sentences describing the same weather, but using original similes rather than the old similes.

105

Write a brief description of a scary movie you've seen. Use strong verbs (*V*) and vivid descriptive adjectives (*DA*). Using the abbreviations, label all verbs and descriptive adjectives.

106

Write a promotion for your favorite television program. Use at least one simple (S), two compound (C), and one complex (CX) sentence. Label the sentence types, using the abbreviations.

107

A nonessential phrase is a phrase that could be omitted from a sentence without altering its meaning: *Dylan, **who enjoys drama,** won the lead in the play. Who enjoys drama* is a nonessential clause; the meaning of the sentence is not changed if it is removed: *Dylan won the lead in the play.*

An **essential phrase,** on the other hand, is a phrase necessary to the meaning of the sentence: *The teachers **planning to go on the field trip** changed their lesson plans. Planning to go on the field trip* is an essential phrase; it cannot be omitted without changing the meaning of the sentence (not all the teachers changed their lesson plans, only those who were planning to go on the field trip).

108

Use three essential (*E*) and three nonessential (*NE*) phrases in sentences to describe people or animals. Label the phrases, using the abbreviations.

Write a simple recipe for a food you enjoy. Highlight the verbs. What type of sentence did you use the most: declarative, interrogative, imperative, or exclamatory?

Write a short restaurant review for a local eating place. Use seven descriptive adjectives. Highlight the adjectives.

110

Write a descriptive paragraph describing a favorite outfit you have or would like to have. Use at least five vivid descriptive adjectives. Underline the adjectives.

111

List six actions that someone involved in your favorite sport would take. Write two or three sports page headlines using these verbs. Circle the verbs.

112

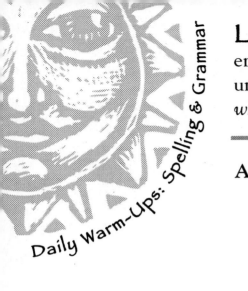

List ten adverbs to communicate different emotions. Use five of these adverbs in sentences, and underline them. (Example: *My teacher sighed* **heavily** *when everyone failed the test.*)

Adverbs

Sentences

In the space below, write an e-mail to a friend, using six slang expressions. Then rewrite the message in standard English.

Informal E-mail

Standard English

114

Write sentences using each pair of these often-confused words: *coarse/course; complement/ compliment; formally/formerly; plain/plane.*

115

Make a list of seven subordinating conjunctions. Introduce seven subordinate clauses with the subordinating conjunctions. Then use the subordinate clauses in three complex sentences. Underline the subjects of the subordinate clauses once and the predicates twice.

116

Write three sentences with slang expressions. Revise the sentences, changing the slang expressions to standard English. When is it acceptable to use slang? When should you use standard English?

117

Write three run-on sentences.

Now change the run-ons into complete sentences.

Write two examples of how to use **capitals** in titles for the following: newspapers, magazines, works of art, movies, and television programs. Which words do you *not* capitalize?

119

Write five sentences with dangling modifiers. Correct them and tell why the original sentences were not clear.

120

Give two examples showing the correct use of **abbreviations** in each of the following: titles used with names, units of measure, and street addresses.

Make up three riddles, each having a common noun as an answer. Exchange papers with a partner, and figure out the riddles. Exchange papers again to check answers.

122

Write five sentences containing a compound object. Exchange papers with a partner. Have your partner replace one object with an object pronoun. Here's an example: *The teacher asked Sean and Elena to clean up* becomes *The teacher asked Sean and* **me** *to clean up* or *The teacher asked Elena and* **him** *to clean up.*

123

Write a sentence for each often-confused word: *lose/loose; moral/morale; peace/piece; pain/pane; principal/principle; quiet/quite*. Underline the words.

124

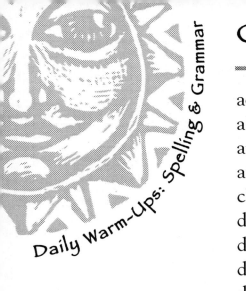

Correct these commonly misspelled words.

acquaintence
alright
analize
atheletics
challange
definitly
dependant
develope
disapear

Now use the corrected words in a paragraph and highlight them.

125

Write three sentences containing parentheses.

126

When do you capitalize the first letter of a sentence within the parentheses?

When don't you capitalize it?

Write a humorous dialogue,

alternating writing dialogue lines with a partner.

Now turn all the direct quotations into indirect quotations.

127

Unscramble the following jumbled

words that are often misspelled or confused with

other words.

tysrtaaion

rtshtgai

rethi

tsaiw

rhewate

htheerw

shwoe

ryuo

128

Daily Warm-Ups: Spelling & Grammar

Correct these commonly misspelled words.

disapoint

embarras

especialy

exagerate

excitment

exausted

fasinating

grammer

humorus

immediatly

129

Think of three comma rules (you may use a grammar book for reference). Write two sentences to show each rule in action. Circle the commas and write the corresponding comma rule beside each sentence.

130

Write two examples showing when **italics** (or underlining, in handwritten work) are used when referring to the following: newspapers, films, television programs, books, and magazines. Use underlining if you're writing by hand, italics if you're using a computer.

131

© 2002 J. Weston Walch, Publisher

Write three sentences using a **question mark** inside quotation marks.

132

Write two sentences using a question mark outside quotation marks.

For each sentence you wrote, write a brief explanation for the placement of the question mark.

Possessives show ownership and

use an **apostrophe:** *the **dog's** bone; the **girls'** locker room.*

Form the possessive of five singular nouns.

Form the possessive of five plural nouns ending in *s.*

133

Write a rule for forming the possessive of singular nouns and
one for forming the possessive of plural nouns ending in *s.*

Write a paragraph using at least five of the following expressions: *I am; let us; they had; is not; do not; should not; cannot.*

134

Now write **contractions** above the expressions in your paragraph. How does the second paragraph sound different from the first?

Write a radio commercial for a food you like, using at least four **onomatopoetic words** (words that sound like what they represent, such as *crash* or *thump* or *plop*.)

Write a rhymed poem, using at least three of each: nouns (N), verbs (V), adjectives (ADJ), and adverbs (ADV). Exchange poems with a partner, and label each part of speech with the abbreviations.

136

Create a comic strip with a school setting. Use at least two linking verbs and two action verbs in the dialogue.

137

Write six silly run-on sentences. Make up an answer key, changing the run-ons to complete sentences. Exchange your run-on sentences with a partner for correction. After writing answers, switch papers again to correct.

138

Write at least six lines of lyrics to a popular song. Label verbs (*V*), nouns (*N*), and adjectives (*ADJ*).

139

Design a crossword puzzle using at least ten proper nouns. Make up an answer key. Exchange puzzles with a partner. Exchange papers again to check answers.

Form the plural of the nouns below.

tomato

hero

veto

potato

torpedo

Now write the spelling rule to describe how you formed the plurals above.

141

Write the plurals of these following nouns formed in irregular ways.

tooth

goose

woman

foot

child

mouse

sheep

trout

moose

deer

142

Correct these commonly misspelled words and circle the trouble spot in each word.

labortory

marrage

mischeivous

occassionally

pasttime

permanant

perseverence

posess

potatoe

recieve

referal

143

Compile a list of six overused adjectives, such as *great* and *awesome*. Using these adjectives, write a paragraph about a movie you enjoy. Then revise your paragraph by writing vivid, specific adjectives. Write them above the overused ones.

144

Write a free verse poem, using at least five prepositional phrases. Exchange papers with a partner and circle the prepositions. Exchange papers again to correct.

145

Write a review of a CD by your favorite musical group. Use at least one simple sentence (*S*), one compound sentence (*C*), and two complex sentences (*CPX*). Write the abbreviations for the sentence types above the sentences.

146

Write three sentences with appositives, describing people you know or places you've been. Underline the appositives. Remember the commas!

147

Write five compound sentences.

Exchange papers with a partner. Change each of your partner's compound sentences to a complex sentence. Then exchange papers again to check answers.

148

Write two sentences for each of the following indefinite pronouns: *one*, *neither*, and *each*. Use a prepositional phrase after each pronoun. Highlight the pronouns and circle the verbs.

149

Write two sentences for each of the following **indefinite pronouns:** *both*, *few*, *many*, and *several*. Underline the pronouns and circle the verbs. Did you use a singular or a plural verb with these pronouns?

150

Some indefinite pronouns may be singular or plural: *all*, *any*, *most*, *none*, and *some*. Write a sentence for each pronoun. Underline the pronouns and circle the verbs. Tell whether the pronouns are singular or plural in each sentence. Explain why.

151

Write three sentences with compound subjects joined by *and*. Highlight the compound subjects and circle the verbs. Write a rule for using verbs with compound subjects.

152

Write three sentences with singular subjects joined by *or*. Underline the singular subjects and circle the verbs.

153

Write a sentence for each of these nouns: *economics*, *genetics*, *measles*, *news*, *mathematics*, *electronics*. Circle the verbs. Did you use singular or plural verbs? Why?

154

Write four sentences with both direct objects (*DO*) and indirect objects (*IO*). Using the abbreviations, label all objects.

What questions did you need to ask to find the direct and indirect objects?

155

Write three sentences with compound objects of the preposition. Make one object in each sentence an object pronoun. Highlight all the object pronouns. Can you think of a trick to help you find the correct object pronoun? Write it to share with a partner. Did you come up with the same trick?

156

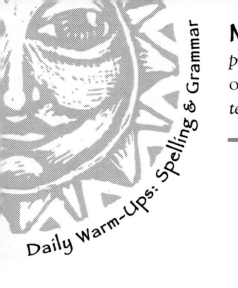

Make a three-column chart labeled *present, past,* and *past participle*. Put the correct forms of the following verbs in the appropriate spaces: *swim, teach, lead, fight, lose, spin, stand,* and *swing.*

157

Make a three-column chart

labeled *positive*, *comparative*, and *superlative*. Fill in the chart, listing the three degrees of these adjectives: *neat*, *good*, *fast*, *honest*, *funny*, *punctual*, and *clean*.

158

Write a paragraph about your favorite sport, using at least four **misplaced modifiers** (MM). Exchange papers with a partner, and correct the misplaced modifiers. Exchange papers again to check corrections.

159

Write three sentences with

nonessential clauses (*NE*) and three sentences with essential clauses (*E*). Label the clauses with the corresponding abbreviations. What is the difference between the two types of clauses?

160

Write a sentence using commas for each of the following situations: introductory expressions, direct address, dates and addresses, and appositives. Before each sentence, write the applicable comma rule. Circle all commas.

161

An interjection is a word that shows strong feeling. An interjection at the beginning of a sentence is followed by a comma or an exclamation point: **Oh,** *the bus is late again.* or **Gosh!** *That's the loudest thunder clap I've ever heard!*

Write three sentences containing interjections.

Write a paragraph, inserting blanks

for two nouns, two action verbs, one adjective, one adverb, and one interjection. Without reading the paragraph to your partner, ask him or her to provide the missing parts of speech. Write your partner's responses in the appropriate blanks. After you have both filled in the blanks, exchange papers to read the silly results.

163

Write contractions for the following expressions.

I am

let us

they had

we are

you will

is not

should not

were not

Use the contractions in sentences, and underline each contraction

Think of six adverbs to describe the way different animals move. Write a sentence for each of the adverbs. Underline the adverbs, and circle the verbs they modify.

List five interesting adjectives.

Exchange papers with a partner. Write sentences using your partner's adjectives. Underline each adjective, and circle the noun or pronoun each adjective modifies.

166

Sometimes contractions are confused with possessive pronouns. Write a sentence for each contraction below.

it's, who's, you're, they're, there's

Write a sentence for each possessive pronoun below.

its, whose, your, their, theirs

167

Add the suffix *-ly* to the words below to change them from adjectives to adverbs.

casual

final

gentle

simple

168

Now write a rule to explain what you did above.

Add the suffix *-ly* to *ready* and *busy*.

Add the suffix *-ness* to *empty* and *heavy*.

Now complete this sentence to write a spelling rule that applies to the words above: For most words ending in *y*, change the _____ to _____ before adding _____ or _____.

169

Make up a crossword puzzle using the following words often confused: *alter, capital, coarse, dessert, led, lose, personnel, plane, route,* and *principal*. In your clues, make sure you use the words correctly! Exchange puzzles with a partner. Exchange papers again to check answers.

170

Fill in the chart below with five more examples. Make sure all the words are related. An example has been done for you.

Common Noun	Proper Noun	Proper Adjective
country	France	French

171

List five interjections. They may be as common or as unusual as you like. Then exchange your list with a partner. Write a sentence for each of your partner's interjections.

172

Much of your time in school is spent thinking. Write five synonyms for the word *think*. Then use each word in a sentence.

173

Antonyms are words that have the opposite meaning: *hot* and *cold*, *big* and *small*, *up* and *down*. Write five pairs of antonyms (not the ones listed here!).

174

Now imagine that you are teaching a three-year-old about opposites. Write sentences contrasting the words in each pair you wrote above: *The soup is hot. The ice cream is cold.*

Draw a cartoon representing a sentence with a dangling modifier. For example, for the sentence *Walking down the street, the bike hit her,* what do you think the cartoon would look like?

A contronym is a word that has two opposite meanings: *Sanction* means both to approve and to condemn, for example. Write the opposite definitions of each of the following words.

oversight

buckle

cleave

screen

left

176

Using the following format, write a poem about school.

first line: a noun

second line: three adjectives describing the noun

third line: a line expressing an opinion or a feeling about the noun

fourth line: a synonym for the noun, or another related noun

Example:

math book

old, marked up, difficult

I am not a fan of multiplication tables

guide to a headache

177

List five interesting verbs to replace

the word *said*. Then exchange papers with a partner and use his or her words in a dialogue to indicate how each person speaks.

178

Fill in the blanks in the paragraph below with an appropriate word. Above each added word, write what part of speech it is.

The _____ house was _____. Leah decided to _____ it. _____ she tried the door, she turned _____ to the window. It rose easily. _____ climbed _____ the sill and into the hallway. She _____ when she _____ the owner coming down the _____. _____! Where could she hide?

179

Think about your knowledge of spelling and grammar. Write a tip for a future student to help her or him learn something about spelling or grammar that you found challenging.

180

Answers will vary on pages not listed.

13. Fragments and sentences will vary. Complete sentences have a subject and a predicate and express a complete thought. Fragments do not.

14. Sentences will vary. Past tenses: chose, drove, knew, swam, took, went, brought, burst.

16. Answers will vary, but possibilities include firefighter; postal carrier, mail carrier; salesperson, sales associate; businessperson, executive; chairperson, chair. Sentences will vary.

18. Sentences will vary. Uses of capitals include for proper names, for proper adjectives, to begin a sentence, for the word *I*, and in titles.

25. Solutions include: Senators give up their privacy when they run for office. A senator gives up her or his privacy when she or he runs for office. A senator gives up privacy when running for office. Doctors study for many years to learn their profession. A doctor studies many years to learn his or her profession. A doctor studies many years to learn the medical profession.

26. *im*balance, *il*legal, *im*mature, *im*polite, *ir*rational, *in*sane. The prefix *in-* becomes *im-* before words beginning with *m*, *b*, or *p*; *il-* before words beginning with *l*; *ir-* before words beginning with *r*. Words beginning with other letters take *in-*.

29. **bad:** an adjective meaning not good, unfavorable; **badly:** an adverb meaning in a bad manner or to a great degree; **good:** an adjective meaning favorable, agreeable; **well:** an adverb meaning in a good or proper manner, satisfactorily; also used in the phrase "feeling well."

30. The words are exceptions to the rule "*i* before *e* except after *c*." Words will vary.

32. The words are exceptions to the rule "If a word ends in silent *e*, do not drop the *e* before adding a suffix that begins with a consonant."

33. hurriedly; ladies; beautiful; happiness

Daily Warm-Ups: Spelling & Grammar

34. They are examples that double the final consonant before adding a suffix that begins with a vowel. Words will vary.

36. start, started, started; yell, yelled, yelled; stop, stopped, stopped; Rule: To form the past participle of a word ending in a consonant, add *-ed* to the end of the present tense.

37. dove; drew; hurt; froze; read; shook; hit; Stories will vary.

38. (have) frozen; (have) grown; (have) become; (have) done; (have) chosen; (have) known; (have) eaten; Paragraphs will vary.

39. ride, rode, ridden; see, saw, seen; shake, shook, shaken; shrink, shrank, shrunk; speak, spoke, spoken; swim, swam, swum; throw, threw, thrown; write, wrote, written

42. Sentences will vary; sentences should have plural verbs.

47. crises; parentheses; analyses; bases; diagnoses; Rule: To make the plural of Latin and Greek words ending in *-is*, change the *i* to *e*.

49. plural

53. Answers will vary but may include delivery person; may the best person/candidate win; police officer; flight attendant; server; guard, lookout.

55. Words will vary; it is generally preferable to use more direct terms to avoid confusion and wordiness.

63. Ads will vary; most sentences are probably short simple sentences with some compound sentences; people will not put in the effort to read an ad that looks too wordy or demanding. Ads get right to the point.

70. Answers will vary; courses that name languages or that have a section number after them are capitalized.

71. college; pledge; knowledge; mileage; privilege; Sentences will vary.

73. alumnae; cacti; criteria; curricula; octopi;

Sentences will vary.

75. **lie:** to be in a horizontal position; **lay:** to put or set down (takes a direct object, unlike *lie*); **altogether:** completely, wholly; **all together:** everyone in a group; **sit:** to rest on the buttocks; **set:** to put, to lay (takes a direct object)

82. *In view of the fact that* is a wordy way to say "since" or "because"; *might of* and *could of* should be *might have* and *could have*; *between you and I* should be *between you and me*; and *past history* is redundant (all history is past).

84. acknowledgment; bankruptcy; budget; calendar; changeable; commitment; deterrent; correspondence

85. Answers may vary: bar, ass; quip; for, it; gram, mar, am; arch, era; know, ledge; Memory tricks will vary.

92. Sentences will vary; **beside:** next to; **besides:** in addition to; **can:** to be able to; **may:** to be allowed to; **compare:** to show how two or more things are similar; **contrast:** to show how things are different.

93. calves; elves; halves; leaves; loaves; shelves; thieves; Rule: To form the plural of a word ending in *f*, change the *f* to *v* and add *es*.

94. boxes; foxes; lunches; messes; taxes; waltzes; Rule: If a word ends in an *s* sound, add *es* to form the plural.

95. Nouns will vary; **abstract nouns** name intangibles, such as qualities, ideas, or emotions; **concrete nouns** name things that can be sensed.

117. Sentences will vary; slang may be used in informal conversations and correspondence, or in dialogue for stylistic effect, but in all formal writing and speaking, standard English should be used.

119. Examples will vary; articles, coordinating conjunctions, and short prepositions are not capi-

talized, unless it is the first word of the title.

125. acquaintance; all right; analyze; athletics; challenge; definitely; dependent; develop; disappear; Sentences will vary.

126. Sentences will vary. Capitalize the first letter within parentheses if it is the start of a new sentence; do not capitalize if it is enclosed within the main sentence.

128. stationary; straight; their; waist; weather; whether; whose; your

129. disappoint; embarrass; especially; exaggerate; excitement; exhausted; fascinating; grammar; humorous; immediately

134. contractions: I'm; let's; they'd; isn't; don't; shouldn't; can't

141. tomatoes; heroes; vetoes; potatoes; torpedoes; Rule: If a word ends in *o*, form its plural by adding *es*.

142. teeth; geese; women; feet; children; mice; sheep; trout; moose; deer

143. laboratory; marriage; mischievous; occasionally; pastime; permanent; perseverance; possess; potato; receive; referral

150. Sentences will vary; all take plural verbs.

154. These words take singular verbs.

155. Answers will vary; to find the direct object, ask *Who?* or *What?*; to find the indirect object, ask *To whom?* or *To what?*

157. swim, swam, swum; teach, taught, taught; lead, led, led; fight, fought, fought; lose, lost, lost; spin, spun, spun; stand, stood, stood; swing, swung, swung

158. neat, neater, neatest; good, better, best; fast, faster, fastest; honest, more honest, most honest; funny, funnier, funniest; punctual, more punctual, most punctual; clean, cleaner, cleanest

160. Sentences will vary; nonessential clauses can be removed without changing the meaning of the sentence; essential clauses cannot.

164. I'm; let's; they'd; we're; you'll; isn't; shouldn't; weren't; Sentences will vary.
168. casually; finally; gently; simply; Rule: When adding the suffix *-ly* to a word ending in *l*, add *ly*. If a word ends in an *l* followed by silent *e*, drop the *e* before adding *y*.
169. readily; busily; emptiness; heaviness; Rule: Change the *y* to *i* before adding *-ly* or *-ness*.
176. oversight: supervision, neglect; buckle: join together, collapse; cleave: stick together, cut apart; screen: to hide from view, to show; left: departed, remained